GUI

NABUCCO

Overture to the Opera

Ernst Eulenburg Ltd

London · Mainz · Madrid · New York · Paris · Prague · Tokyo · Toronto · Zürich

CONTENTS

© 2012 Ernst Eulenburg & Co GmbH, Mainz
for Europe excluding the British Isles
Ernst Eulenburg Ltd, London
for all other countries

All rights reserved.
No part of this publication may be reproduced, stored in a retrieval system,
or transmitted in any form or by any means,
electronic, mechanical, photocopying, recording or otherwise,
without the prior written permission of the publisher:

Ernst Eulenburg Ltd
48 Great Marlborough Street
London W1F 7BB

PREFACE

The years that had preceded the composition of Verdi's *Nabucco* were not exactly happy ones. His wife Margherita had died in June 1840 only four years after their wedding. Two years before the couple had to cope with the death of their first-born child Virginia and a year later they also lost their son Icilio Romano. Neither of the two children survived its second year of life. The extremely successful premiere of his *Oberto* at La Scala, Milan, in November 1839 nevertheless gave Verdi a brief moment of happiness and brought in other commissions. However, the opera *Un giorno di regno*, composed the year his wife died, turned out to be a fiasco. It received only a single performance, and Verdi even played with the idea of bidding the stage farewell. Only at the insistence of the impresario Bartolomeo Merelli did the composer change his mind.[1] Merelli handed over to Verdi the libretto to *Nabucodonosor* (Nebuchadnezzar) which he had already unsuccessfully offered to Otto Nicolai for setting. Originally Verdi was to have set to music *Il proscritto* by the librettist Gaetano Rossi. However, after Nicolai had rejected *Nabucco* because of its brutal content, he ultimately took over Rossi's text. The choice, though, did not bring him success. Nicolai's *Il Proscritto* failed with the public and at that point left behind a deep break in a professional as well as also in a private sense. Thus, after requesting an early cancellation of his contract with Merelli, Nicolai turned his back on Italy and also on his relation with the singer Erminia Frezzolini who – as protagonist of the work was suffering on-stage the full effects of the merciless reaction of the audience – was broken by the desolate performance.[2]

Verdi, on the other hand, was granted a great triumph with the *Nabucco* scorned by Nicolai; even Erminia Frezzolini – now prima donna in two of Verdi's operas – was able to look forward to a more brilliant heyday in the not too-distant future. And yet Verdi also seems for a moment to have turned away from the piece, if one believes a contemporary report that Verdi himself (in retrospect at least) declared as trustworthy. The text of 'Va pensiero, sull'ali dorate' ('Fly, thought, on golden wings', the 'Chorus of the Hebrew Slaves') is alleged to have gripped Verdi from the first moment and probably contributed to his acceptance of the commission.[3] The libretto for *Nabucodonosor* was written by Temistocle Solera who, concerning the central plot lines, could orient himself to the play *Nabuchodonosor* by Auguste Anicet-Bourgeois and Francis Cornu dating from 1836 as well as to the ballet *Nabuccodonosor* by Antonio Cortesi and premiered in the same year, at La Scala, Milan. Apart from some changes and/or additions Solera's libretto differed from its models in one essential detail: the strong accentuation of the choral scenes ascribing to the people a new quality and, occasionally, the same importance as an individual character. Such a treatment of the chorus

---

[1] see Fabrizio Della Seta, 'Verdi', in: *MGG²ᴾ*, Vol.16 (Kassel, etc., 2006), col. 1440

[2] see Julian Budden, *The Operas of Verdi*. Vol.1: *From Oberto to Rigoletto* (London, 1973), 92f.

[3] see Budden, ibid., 91f.

was, however, not altogether new. The influence of Rossini's *Mosé in Egitto* seems obvious; there also the chorus steps forward in the guise of the Israelite people not only as decorative accessory, but as plot carrier.[4]

After some initial doubts Verdi began work on *Nabucodonosor* in the first half of 1841 and submitted the completed score in the fall of the same year. The premiere, however, took place on 9 March 1842 at La Scala, Milan, which delay was probably not entirely unclouded by previous differences concerning the production design of the opera. Whereupon Merelli gratefully seized the opportunity thus offered to reduce the costs and resorted to the already available costumes and decor of the *Nabuccodonosor* ballet performed four years previously.[5] All the more gratifying for Verdi, therefore, must have been the brilliant success of the premiere – which not even the rather middling vocal achievement of the prima donna could diminish. Already on the first night, 'Va pensiero' sent the audience into raptures, so much so that the ensemble could not leave the stage without a corresponding encore. In the period following the premiere, the opera underwent some small revisions. Besides the interventions in the extremely demanding part of Abigaille, Verdi even relinquished her death scene and ended the opera with the chorus 'Immenso Jehova' instead.[6] In a performance in Brussels in 1848, moreover, ballet music written by Verdi (now lost) was supposed to have been heard.

The eight performances during the approaching end of the spring season were followed by a mature record 57 further performances in the fall season at La Scala. The cornerstone for Verdi's career as 'leading Italian opera composer of the young generation'[7] was laid. In Italy over 40 opera houses programmed *Nabucodonosor*. Only a year after the premiere Donizetti conducted the work in Vienna – the first Verdi opera to be performed in that city. Other productions followed – amongst them Stuttgart and Berlin in 1844 – but always under the rather awkward title *Nabucodonosor*. The work's title was finally shortened to *Nabucco* at a performance in Corfu in 1844; the opera was even renamed *Nino* for a London performance in 1846, in order to obscure the Biblical subject, since the stage representation of biblical characters was regarded as inappropriate.[8] For Verdi the success of *Nabucco* marked the beginning of his 'galley' years that were indeed determined by hard work, but ultimately also assured his financial independence.[9]

The overture to *Nabucco* draws its musical substance from the work's rich fund of melodies.[10] But the opera is introduced by a passage that, first and foremost, sets an atmospheric mood rather than taking up specific quotations: a chorale-like melody, intoned by three trombones and cimbasso,[11] dominates the first bars until a bloodcurdling *ff* entrance of the orchestra (b9) brings it to an abrupt halt.

[4] see Michael Walter, 'Nabucodonosor', in: *Verdi-Handbuch* (Kassel, Stuttgart, Weimar, 2001), 312
[5] see Budden, ibid., 93
[6] see Roger Parker, 'Nabucodonosor', in: *Pipers Enzyklopädie des Musiktheaters*, Vol.6 (Munich, 1997), 391

[7] see Walter, ibid., 314
[8] see Budden, ibid., 112
[9] see Walter, ibid., col. 1440
[10] Budden, ibid., offers a detailed musical analysis of the opera. The overture is treated on pages 96 and 97.
[11] Cimbasso, a bass or contrabass valve trombone introduced by Verdi to replace the ophicleide

A few bars later the chorale again enters unperturbed. The sombre, yet august sounds descriptively mediate the basic mood of the opera, marked by persecution, but likewise by intransigence, that dominates the struggle of the Hebrew people against the Babylonian King Nebuchadnezzar. The chorale is ultimately superseded by a melody that runs through the overture formally, namely the chorus 'Il maledetto non ha fratelli' from Act 2, in which Ismaele, the nephew of the king of Jerusalem, is cursed by the Levites on account of his reckless conduct for the love of Nabucco's daughter. The contempt of the disappointed Hebrews speaks unmistakeably out of the short staccato melodic fragments. The choral music soon resumes – from the now inserted heart of *Nabucco*, 'Va pensiero'. The slave chorus does not occur in its original guise, but in a curiously distorted form (bb53ff). Instead of 4/4 metre chosen for the chorus, it is heard in the overture in a 3/8 metre that causes the familiar rhythmic structure to sway. Likewise, with the second entrance of the famous theme (b88) the combination of oboe and trumpets carrying the melody – which attempts to lend the music a certain pathos but which is, however, contradicted by the jaunty chatter of flutes, clarinets and violins – provides for a moment of surprise. Other views of central scenes follow before the 'Il maledetto' melody releases the listener – probably not without dark foreboding – to the incidents on-stage.

Sandra Borzikowski
Translation: Margit L. McCorkle

VORWORT

Es waren nicht gerade glückliche Jahre, die der Komposition von Verdis *Nabucco* vorausgegangen waren. Nur vier Jahre nach der Hochzeit starb im Juni 1840 seine Frau Margherita. Zwei Jahre zuvor hatte das Paar den Tod ihrer Erstgeborenen Virginia bewältigen müssen und ein Jahr später verloren sie auch noch ihren Sohn Icilio Romano. Keines der beiden Kinder vollendete das zweite Lebensjahr. Die äußerst erfolgreiche Uraufführung seines *Oberto* in der Mailänder Scala im November 1839 bereitete Verdi immerhin einen kurzen Moment des Glücks und brachte weitere Kompositionsaufträge ein. Doch die im Todesjahr seiner Frau entstandene Oper *Un giorno di regno* geriet zum Fiasko. Es blieb bei dieser einmaligen Aufführung und Verdi spielte gar mit dem Gedanken, sich von der Bühne zu verabschieden. Lediglich auf Drängen des Impresarios Bartolomeo Merelli hin, ließ sich der Komponist erweichen.[1] Merelli händigte Verdi das Libretto zu *Nabucodonosor* aus, das er bereits Otto Nicolai erfolglos zur Vertonung angeboten hatte. Ursprünglich sollte Verdi *Il proscritto* des Librettisten Gaetano Rossi in Musik setzen. Doch nachdem Nicolai *Nabucco* auf Grund seines brutalen Inhaltes abgelehnt hatte, übernahm dieser schließlich Rossis Text. Erfolg brachte ihm die Wahl allerdings nicht ein. Nicolais *Il Proscritto* fiel beim Publikum durch und hinterließ damit einen tiefen Einschnitt sowohl in beruflicher als auch in privater Hinsicht. So kehrte Nicolai nach der erbetenen vorzeitigen Lösung seines Vertragsverhältnisses mit Merelli nicht nur Italien den Rücken, auch seine Beziehung zur Sängerin Erminia Frezzolini, die als Protagonistin des Stückes die gnadenlose Reaktion des Publikums noch auf der Bühne zu spüren bekam, zerbrach an der desolaten Vorstellung.[2]

Ein großer Triumph hingegen war Verdi mit dem von Nicolai verschmähten *Nabucco* beschieden (und auch Erminia Frezzolini sollte im Übrigen in nicht allzu ferner Zukunft – nun u. a. als Primadonna in zwei Opern Verdis – glanzvolleren Zeiten entgegensehen). Und doch scheint auch Verdi das Stück im ersten Moment zurückgewiesen zu haben, glaubt man einem Zeitzeugenbericht, den Verdi selbst im Nachhinein zumindest für zuverlässig erklärt hat. Es sollen die Textzeilen des Chores „Va pensiero" gewesen sein, die Verdi angeblich vom ersten Augenblick an gefesselt und wohl auch zur Annahme des Kompositionsauftrages beigetragen haben.[3] Das Libretto zu *Nabucodonosor* stammte von Temistocle Solera, der sich bezüglich der zentralen Handlungsstränge an dem Schauspiel *Nabuchodonosor* von Auguste Anicet-Bourgeois und Francis Cornu aus dem Jahr 1836 sowie dem im gleichen Jahr – in der Mailänder Scala – uraufgeführten Ballett *Nabuccodonosor* von Antonio Cortesi orientieren konnte. Abgesehen von einigen Änderungen bzw. Hinzufügungen unterscheidet sich Soleras

[1] Vgl. Fabrizio Della Seta: „Verdi", in: *MGG²ᴾ*, Bd. 16, Kassel, usw. 2006, Sp. 1440.

[2] Vgl. Julian Budden: *The Operas of Verdi –* Volume 1: *From Oberto to Rigoletto*, London 1973, S. 92f.

[3] Vgl. Budden, S. 91f.

Libretto in einem wesentlichen Punkt von seinen Vorlagen: die starke Akzentuierung von Chorszenen, durch die dem Volk eine neue Qualität und zumindest zeitweise die gleiche Bedeutung wie dem Individuum beigemessen wird. Gänzlich neu war eine solche Behandlung der Chöre jedoch nicht. Der Einfluss von Rossinis *Mosè in Egitto* scheint auf der Hand zu liegen, auch dort tritt der Chor in Gestalt des israelitischen Volkes nicht nur als schmückendes Beiwerk, sondern als Handlungsträger hervor.[4]

Nach den anfänglichen Zweifeln nahm Verdi die Arbeit an *Nabucodonosor* in der ersten Jahreshälfte 1841 auf und noch im Herbst desselben Jahres lag die vollendete Komposition vor. Die Uraufführung fand allerdings erst am 9. März 1842 im Mailänder Teatro alla Scala statt, wohl nicht ganz ungetrübt von vorausgegangenen Differenzen bezüglich der Ausstattung der Oper. Denn Merelli nahm dankbar die sich bietende Gelegenheit zur Kostenreduzierung wahr und griff auf bereits vorhandene Kostüme und Dekoration des vier Jahre zuvor aufgeführten *Nabuccodonosor*-Balletts zurück.[5] Umso befriedigender dürfte der fulminante Erfolg der Uraufführung – den selbst die wohl eher mäßige Gesangsleistung der Primadonna nicht schmälern konnte – für Verdi gewesen sein. Schon am Premierenabend versetzte „Va pensiero" das Publikum in Begeisterung, sodass das Ensemble nicht ohne eine entsprechende Zugabe die Bühne verlassen konnte. In der Folgezeit wurde die Oper noch einigen kleinen Revisionen unterzogen. Neben den Eingriffen in die extrem anspruchsvolle Partie der Abigaille verzichtete Verdi auch auf deren Sterbeszene und ließ die Oper nun mit dem Chor „Immenso Jehova" enden.[6] In einer Brüsseler Aufführung des Jahres 1848 soll überdies eine heute verschollene Ballettmusik aus der Feder Verdis zu hören gewesen sein.

Den acht Aufführungen der bereits ihrem Ende entgegengehenden Saison folgten rekordreife 57 weitere Aufführungen in der Herbstspielzeit der Scala. Der Grundstein für Verdis Karriere als „führender italienischer Opernkomponist der jungen Generation"[7] war gelegt. In Italien nahmen über 40 Opernhäuser *Nabucodonosor* in ihr Programm auf. Nur ein Jahr nach der Uraufführung dirigierte Donizetti das Werk in Wien – es war die erste Verdi-Oper, die es in die k. und k. Metropole an der Donau geschafft hatte. Weitere Stationen – darunter Stuttgart und Berlin im Jahr 1844 – folgten, stets unter dem etwas umständlichen Titel *Nabucodonosor*. Erst anlässlich einer Aufführung in Korfu 1844 wurde der Werktitel schließlich zu *Nabucco* verkürzt und 1846 wurde die Oper für eine Londoner Vorstellung gar in *Nino* umgetauft, um das biblische Sujet zu verschleiern, da man die Darstellung von Charakteren der Heiligen Schrift auf der Bühne unangemessen fand.[8] Für Verdi markierte der Erfolg *Nabuccos* den Beginn seiner „Galeerenjahre", die zwar von harter Arbeit bestimmt waren, ihm aber letztlich auch die finanzielle Unabhängigkeit sicherten.[9]

Die Ouvertüre zu *Nabucco* schöpft ihre musikalische Substanz vor allem aus dem

---

[4] Vgl. Michael Walter: „Nabucodonosor", in: *Verdi-Handbuch*, Kassel, Stuttgart, Weimar 2001, S. 312.
[5] Vgl. Budden, S. 93.

[6] Vgl. Roger Parker: „Nabucodonosor", in: *Pipers Enzyklopädie des Musiktheaters*, Bd. 6, München 1997, S. 391.
[7] Walter, S. 314.
[8] Vgl. Budden, S. 112.
[9] Vgl. Walter, Sp. 1440.

reichen Melodien-Fundus des Stückes.[10] Eingeleitet wird die Oper aber durch eine Passage, die in erster Linie ein atmosphärisches Stimmungsbild schafft anstatt konkrete musikalische Zitate aufzugreifen: Eine choralartige Melodie, intoniert von drei Posaunen sowie einem Cimbasso[11], beherrscht die ersten Takte bis ein markerschütternder *ff*-Einsatz des Orchesters (T. 9) unvermittelt Einhalt gebietet. Doch nur wenige Takte später setzt unbeirrt wieder der Choral ein. Die düsteren, doch zugleich erhabenen Klänge vermitteln anschaulich die von Verfolgung, aber ebenso auch von Unnachgiebigkeit geprägte Grundstimmung der Oper, die den Kampf des hebräischen Volkes gegen den babylonischen König Nabucodonosor nachzeichnet. Abgelöst wird der Choral schließlich von einer Melodie, die die Ouvertüre förmlich durchzieht. Es handelt sich um den Chor „Il maledetto non ha fratelli" aus dem 2. Akt, in dem Ismaele, der Neffe des Königs von Jerusalem, wegen seines rücksichtslosen Verhaltens aus Liebe zur Tochter Nabuccos von den Leviten verflucht wird. Aus den kurzen, staccato gespielten Melodiefragmenten spricht unüberhörbar die Verachtung der enttäuschten Hebräer. Die Chormusik wird bald darauf abermals ertönen – nach dem nun einsetzenden Herzstück *Nabuccos*: „Va pensiero". Der Gefangenenchor tritt allerdings nicht in seiner ursprünglichen, sondern in einer eigentümlich verzerrten Gestalt auf (T. 53ff). Anstelle des für den Chor gewählten 4/4-Taktes ist in der Ouvertüre ein 3/8-Takt zu hören, der das vertraute rhythmische Gerüst ins Wanken bringt. Und auch beim zweiten Einsatz des berühmten Themas (T. 88) sorgt die Verbindung von Oboe und Trompete als Melodieträger – die redlich bemüht scheinen, der Musik einen gewissen Pathos zu verleihen, jedoch konterkariert werden vom unbeschwerten Geplapper der Flöten, Klarinette und Violinen – für einen Überraschungsmoment. Weitere Ausblicke auf zentrale Szenen folgen, ehe die „Il maledetto"-Melodie den Zuhörer – wohl nicht ohne dunkle Vorahnung – in die Geschehnisse auf der Bühne entlässt.

Sandra Borzikowski

---

[10] Eine ausführliche musikalische Analyse der Oper bietet Budden. Die Ouvertüre wird auf den Seiten 96 u. 97 behandelt.

[11] Es handelt sich um eine Bass- oder Kontrabass-Ventilposaune.

NABUCCO

Overture to the Opera

Guiseppe Verdi
(1813–1901)

© 2012 Ernst Eulenburg Ltd, London
and Ernst Eulenburg & Co GmbH, Mainz

No. 1112   EE 6048

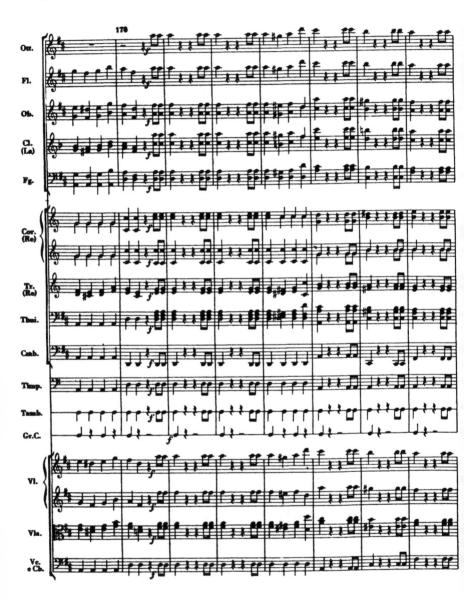

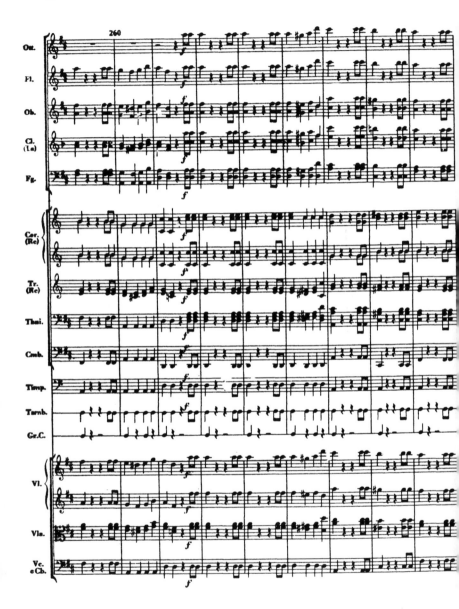

35